Publisher
Robyn Moore

AbstractStudioComics.com
TerryMooreArt.com

Cover Color
Steve Hamaker

Published by Abstract Studio, Inc.,
P. O. Box 271487, Houston, TX 77277-1487.

MOTOR GIRL

by
Terry Moore

"I believe alien life is quite common
in the universe, although intelligent life is less so.
Some say it has yet to appear on planet Earth."
—Stephen Hawking

IS THIS ABOUT THE GUY ON HIS CELL PHONE?

HE WAS DRIVING AN F250! IF YOU'RE POSTING ON FACEBOOK FROM AN F250, YOU'RE A 3-TON **KILLING MACHINE!**

HE COULD ATOMIZE A FIAT AND NEVER KNOW IT!

HE'S BASICALLY A **DEATH STAR!**

HE DIDN'T HIT ANYTHING.

HE'S **GOING** TO!

BUT WHOEVER HE HITS WON'T KNOW WHAT HIT 'EM BECAUSE THEY'LL BE ON THE PHONE, TOO!

THAT'S NOT THE END OF CIVILIZATION—

THAT'S THINNING THE HERD.

YEAH, BUT IT BRINGS ABOUT THE INSTRUMENT OF OUR DESTRUCTION.

WHICH IS...?

DRIVERLESS CARS!

OH, HERE WE GO AGAIN.

A NATION THAT CAN'T DRIVE, CAN'T THRIVE!

THAT A FACT?

DOCUMENTED, MY FRIEND. DOCUMENTED.

DID THE BYZANTINE EMPIRE DRIVE? THE ANCIENT EGYPTIANS? THE ROMANS? NO. AND WHERE ARE THEY NOW? GONE, AND THEY ALL MADE THE SAME MISTAKE...

THEY DIDN'T HAVE DRIVERLESS CARS.

NO, BUT...

THEY GOT RICH AND FAT AND LET SOMEBODY ELSE TAKE THE WHEEL. IT'S THE SAME THING.

THEY DIDN'T HAVE STEERING WHEELS, EITHER.

DON'T ARGUE WITH ME. WE'RE GOING TO NEED EACH OTHER WHEN THE ZOMBIE APOCALYPSE COMES, WHICH SHOULD BE ANY DAY NOW.

GOOD. THEN THE ANIMAL KINGDOM WILL RULE AGAIN.

NOPE.

WHO THEN?

THE UFOS, OF COURSE.

IT'S HOT TODAY, WHAT DOES THE THERMOMETER SAY?

114.

THAT'S WHY I WANT TO GET OUT OF THIS TOWN...

SEE A TREE, TOUCH A DOOR HANDLE WITHOUT GETTING SECOND DEGREE BURNS.

WE'RE RUNNING LOW ON COKE ZERO.

A RACE CAR DRIVER... THAT'S WHAT I SHOULD HAVE BEEN. PEOPLE ACTUALLY PAY YOU TO GO TO CITIES ALL OVER THE WORLD AND DRIVE FAST.

WHAT COULD BE BETTER?

LYING IN A HAMMOCK BY THE BEACH, BEER ON ICE, FISH ON THE GRILL... WATCHING THE GIRLS PLAY VOLLEYBALL.

THAT WAS A RHETORICAL QUESTION.

THEY ASK ME TO JOIN IN.

POP!

TYPITY TYPE!

John,
Yes, I have the piston you're looking for.

YOU DONE?

BUT I CAN'T, SEE? 'CAUSE I'M THERE WITH SCARLETT JOHANSSON... AND SHE GETS JELLYYYY...

OMIGOD, SHUT UP.

AND THEY START WRASSLINNN...

HONK! HONK!

HMM... MID '60'S PLYMOUTH. BATTERY SOUNDS WEAK.

THAT CAN MEAN ONLY ONE THING...

LIBBY.

HEY, LIBBY.

I HAVE ARRIVED!

I SEE THAT.

WARM ENOUGH FOR YA?

114.

OOO DOGEY!

WHAT BRINGS YOU OUT HERE?

BUYER.

BUYER?

YEP.

RICH GUY WANTS TO BUY THIS PLACE.

BUY THE YARD?!

DANG... IT'S HOT IN HERE, TOO!

WHAT DID YOU SAY?

I SAID I'D HAVE TO TALK TO SAM FIRST.

YOU'RE OUT OF COKE ZERO?

BOTTOM SHELF.

11

SO, SAM...

WHAT DO YOU THINK?

SPITZ!

THIS IS WHAT YOU WANTED. GOODBYE JUNKYARD, HELLO WORLD.

I CAN'T AFFORD TO TRAVEL, I DON'T HAVE ANY MONEY.

YOU HAVE $32,000 IN YOUR SAVINGS ACCOUNT.

I'M NOT TOUCHING THAT, IT'S FOR MOM.

SAMANTHA?

ARE YOU OKAY?

OH, SORRY.

YOU WANNA SIT DOWN? IT'S HOT IN HERE.

NO, I'M FINE, REALLY.

YOU KIND OF SPACED OUT ON ME THERE.

YOU'VE BEEN DOING THAT A LOT LATELY. YOU STILL GETTING THOSE HEADACHES?

FROM TIME TO TIME.

YOU SHOULD SEE A DOCTOR.

LIBBY...

SERIOUSLY.

SAM... LOOK AT ME.

I CAN'T IMAGINE WHAT YOU'VE BEEN THROUGH. THREE TOURS OF DUTY...

CAPTURED AND HELD IN SOLITARY CONFINEMENT FOR ALMOST A YEAR....

THAT'S MORE THAN ANYONE SHOULD HAVE TO BEAR, KIDDO. I DON'T KNOW WHERE YOU FOUND THE STRENGTH TO GET THROUGH IT...

BUT YOU DID.

SOMEHOW YOU DID.

13

BUT YOU'RE HOME NOW.

IT'S OKAY TO LET YOUR GUARD DOWN A LITTLE AND TAKE CARE OF YOURSELF... LET A DOCTOR LOOK AT YOU... SEE IF THEY CAN HELP WITH THOSE HEADACHES.

I WILL. I PROMISE.

GOOD. SO, WHAT DO YOU THINK — SHOULD WE SELL THE YARD OR NOT?

IT'S YOUR COMPANY, LIBBY... YOUR DECISION.

NO, NOW, WE'RE IN THIS TOGETHER. I TRUST YOU — YOU'RE LIKE THE DAUGHTER I NEVER HAD.

BUT YOU DO HAVE A DAUGHTER.

EHH, I DON'T LIKE THAT ONE. SHE ONLY WANTS MY MONEY.

THINK ABOUT IT. I'LL CALL YOU TOMORROW.

THIS IS WHAT YOU WANTED.

I... I'M NOT READY.

FLAP!

NOT REAL.
NOT REAL.
WAKE UP.

BOOORG!!!

REAL!

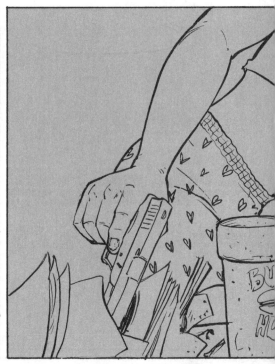

20

21

A LEAK.

LOOKS LIKE 3/4" PIPING.

PROBABLY HYDRAULIC.

CAP THAT EASY.

DON'T DO IT.

UH... EXCUSE ME, HELLO?

BIK?

SAM...

BANG!

SAW A GAZELLE DO THAT ONCE... TURNED AND RAN INTO A TREE, KNOCKED HIMSELF OUT COLD.

POOR LITTLE GUY.

I DON'T KNOW WHAT THIS IS, BUT I CAN SEE WHERE IT'S LEAKING... RIGHT... HERE. WE CAN FIX IT IN TWO MINUTES.

HELLO, E.T.

DON'T TOUCH HIM, HE MIGHT BE RADIOACTIVE.

HE LOOKS LIKE US.

HE'S NOT.

Hey, you're awake,
Welcome to Earth.

WE FIXED YOUR LEAK.

I DON'T KNOW IF THAT'S
WHY YOU BORGED OUT
BUT, MAYBE IT'LL GET
YOU GOING AGAIN.

I DID GOOD?

CLICK!

AWWN...
YOU'RE WELCOME.

OKAY, OKAY,...

WATCH THE
HANDS.

SO, E.T. IS REAL,

AND RUDE.

A LITTLE GRABBY FOR MY TASTE.

BIK WAS NICE,

CLOSE ENCOUNTER.

SAM?

C'MON.

HUH?

`K.

MIKE?

≥GRUNT≤

DID THAT REALLY JUST HAPPEN?

WHAT DO YOU MEAN?

I'M NOT STUPID. I KNOW I HAVE PROBLEMS WITH ... REALITY.

YOU KNOW WHAT'S REAL? E.T.'S PAW PRINTS ON YOUR BUTT.

OMIGOD, YOU'RE JELLY.

GORILLAS DON'T GET JELLY.

OH PLEASE.

"All are lunatics, but he who can analyze
his delusion is called a philosopher."
—Ambrose Bierce

HEY MUNCHKIN...
I HAVE TO GO NOW.
TAKE CARE OF YOUR
MOM WHILE I'M
GONE, OKAY?
...I LOVE YOU.

DAD?

YAWN!

SCRATCH!

GROSS.

SHOULD'A KNOCKED.

I HATE WHEN HE'S RIGHT.

COFFEE.

YAWN!

I HAD THAT DREAM ABOUT MY DAD AGAIN. I COULD HEAR HIS VOICE.

WHAT DOES HE SOUND LIKE?

HOME.

HE SOUNDS LIKE HOME.

IF IT WAS A DREAM, THERE WOULDN'T BE HANDPRINTS ON YOUR FRUIT OF THE LOOMS ...AND A CRUSHED DESOTO IN THE YARD.

WITH GRABBY HANDS. MAYBE MARS NEEDS WOMEN.

IT WAS A CARTOON! FLYING SAUCERS, LITTLE GREEN MEN...

THAT'S RIDICULOUS.

I WENT TO BED ON A FULL STOMACH AND DREAMED ABOUT CARTOON ALIENS.

OKEY DOKEY.

WHEEEE!

KA-BOOM!

HEE! HEE! HEE! HEE!

ANGRY BIRDS MAKE ANGRY GORILLAS.

GULP!

KNOCK! KNOCK! KNOCK!

SPIT!

SOMEBODY'S AT THE DOOR.

WHO?

I DON'T KNOW, I DIDN'T HEAR A CAR.

ME EITHER.

GUN?

NO.

YOU SURE?

GUN TROUBLE DOESN'T KNOCK FIRST, MIKEY.

GRRGH!

MAYBE THEY PARKED OUT ON THE ROAD.

KNOCK! KNOCK! KNOCK!

CAN'T BE UPS, I HEAR THAT TRUCK EVERY TIME.

GUN.

NO.

BIK!

>BLINK<
>BLINK<

BIK?

ARE YOU SEEING THIS?

UH HUH.

NOT A DREAM?

UH UH.

UH... HI. AGAIN.

>AHEM<

BIK BIK BIK BIK.

B-LORP!

WELL THAT DOESN'T LOOK GOOD. WHAT'S THE PROBLEM?

BIK BIK.

JEEZ, WHAT ARE YOU GUYS USING FOR FUEL?

I'LL TAKE A LOOK AT IT.

SAM, WAIT.

34

SO YOU SAW A UFO.

I THINK SO. MAYBE.

DOESN'T SURPRISE ME IN THE LEAST, EVERYBODY I KNOW HAS SEEN A UFO OUT HERE ONE TIME OR ANOTHER.

MAYBE YOU'RE JUST DEHYDRATED.

I'M NOT DEHYDRATED.

DRINK!

DRINK OR YOU'RE GOING STRAIGHT TO BED WITH NO SUPPER!

THAT'S WHAT MOMMA USED TO SAY. SHE COULD REALLY BRING THE PAIN.

NOW I DRINK A MARTINI EVERY DAY AT FIVE...

AND TOAST TO MOMMA.

GULP GULP GULP

BACK IN THE 80s, WE HAD UFOS ALL OVER OUR PROPERTY.

REALLY?

YEP. MY EX WOULD SHOOT AT 'EM.

NO, LIBBY, THAT'S AWFUL.

THAT'S WHAT I TOLD HIM, I SAID, "DON'T DO THAT, YOU OLD FOOL, YOU'LL JUST MAKE 'EM MAD!"

THEY COULD HAVE BEEN AIRPLANES.

I KNOW!

TELL HER... DON'T SELL THE JUNKYARD.

TELL HER HOW YOU FEEL.

I CAN'T DO THAT, IT BELONGS TO HER.

LIBBY, WHAT DID YOU DECIDE ABOUT THE YARD?

ARE YOU GOING TO SELL IT?

LIKE I SAID YESTERDAY—

IT'S UP TO YOU, IF YOU'RE READY TO MOVE ON AND DO SOMETHING ELSE, THEN ALL RIGHT.

YOU MIGHT WANT TO CLEAN OUT YOUR FRIDGE HERE, IT'S SMELLING A LITTLE RIPE.

YOU KNOW YOU CAN'T STAY HERE FOREVER, RIGHT? SOONER OR LATER, YOU HAVE TO GO HOME.

NOT NOW.

YOUR FAMILY MISSES YOU.

PLEASE.

THIS IS THE ONLY EDIBLE THING IN THERE, ONE APPLE JUICE.

LIBBY, ABOUT THE YARD, MAYBE WE COULD...

BANG! BANG! BANG!

INCOMING, SOUNDS HEAVY.

SUV, NEW WITH DETUNED V8.

CRUNCH!

RUMBLE

EXPLODER

RUMBLE

Libby SALVAGE
And Scrap Metal
BUY · SELL · TRADE
"Put some junk in your Tr..."

BRUMMm...

BAM!

DOESN'T LOOK LIKE MUCH.

I DISAGREE. IT'S AN IMPRESSIVE SIGHT, LIKE THE RUINS OF ANOTHER TIME.

PUT A VOLCANO BESIDE IT AND YOU HAVE THE POMPEII OF NEVADA.

IT'S A JUNKYARD... IN THE MIDDLE OF NOWHERE.

I SEE A RUSTY OASIS IN THE DESERT— A SHRINE TO PEOPLE WHO CAME BEFORE US AND LEFT BEHIND THE CARRIAGES OF THEIR DREAMS AND AMBITIONS.

YOU CAN'T TAKE IT WITH YOU.

YOU'RE A NIHILIST, LARRY.

PHHT!

I'M A REALIST, VIC.

NOT EVERY STORY ENDS IN TRAGEDY.

MINE DO.

YOU CHOSE THIS PATH.

I'M GOOD AT WHAT I DO.

SO AM I, BUT THERE'S MORE TO LIFE THAN DEATH.

MAYBE, BUT DEATH PAYS BETTER.

CAN'T TAKE IT WITH YOU, LARRY.

DON'T CARE, VIC.

NIHILIST.

YOU JUST WALK IN WITHOUT KNOCKING?

I'M LOOKING FOR LIBBY.

YOU FOUND HER. WHAT CAN I DO YOU FOR?

MR. WALDEN ASKED ME TO DELIVER THIS TO YOU.

WHAT IS IT?

AN AGREEMENT TO SELL THIS PROPERTY TO MR WALDEN AND A CASHIERS CHECK. SIGN THE AGREEMENT AND THE CHECK IS YOURS.

WHAT ON EARTH DOES MR WALDEN WANT WITH AN OLD JUNKYARD?

I WOULDN'T KNOW, MA'AM.

I'M JUST THE MESSENGER...

HANDING YOU A CHECK WITH A LOT OF ZEROES ON IT.

WHO DO YOU BOYS REALLY WORK FOR?

I WORK FOR MR. WALDEN.

AND WHO DOES HE WORK FOR?

I'M NOT AT LIBERTY TO SAY.

WELL HOW DO I KNOW HE'S NOT BUYING THIS LAND TO STORE NUCLEAR WASTE OR SOMETHING?

I DON'T WANT TO SELL MY PROPERTY TO SOMEBODY WHO'S GOING TO HURT THE ENVIRONMENT.

LIBBY... MA'AM... THIS IS ME, OFFERING YOU ENOUGH MONEY TO LIVE ANYWHERE BUT HERE.

AND THIS IS ME SAYING NO THANKS. NOT UNTIL YOU TELL ME WHAT YOUR PLANS ARE.

I MEAN, IF IT'S A CASINO, THEN I'M GONNA WANT A PERCENTAGE, GET MY DRIFT?

I'M NOT AUTHORIZED TO NEGOTIATE WITH YOU, MA'AM. THIS IS MR. WALDEN'S OFFER, I STRONGLY ADVISE YOU TO TAKE IT. GET MY DRIFT?

ERP!

I DO INDEED. YOU TELL WALDEN TO TAKE THAT ENVELOPE AND SHOVE IT UP HIS NOSE.

LARRY?

I THINK LARRY'S READY TO LEAVE, BIG GUY. TIME TO GO.

41

CAN'T SLEEP?

MM MM.

WOW.

SO WHAT IS IT WITH YOU AND ALIENS?

SOME THINGS ARE BETTER LEFT ALONE.

MEANING?

NOTHING OFF THIS PLANET IS SAFE FOR HUMAN BEINGS.

EXTRATERRESTRIAL LIFE IS ONE OF THE GREAT QUESTIONS AND HERE WE HAVE AN ANSWER ON OUR DOORSTEP.

SOME DOORS ARE BETTER LEFT CLOSED.

WHAT ARE YOU AFRAID OF?

43

DID YOU SEE THAT?!

THEY SPLIT OFF AND HIT THE GAS!? *JEEZ*, THAT WAS *FAST!*

YEAH.

THEY'RE REAL, MIKE. THEY'RE REAL!

EVERYBODY IN THE WORLD WANTS TO KNOW, AND WE KNOW—

THEY'RE REAL!

THERE'S ANOTHER ONE!

WHAT ARE THEY DOING?

KNOCK, KNOCK.

"Two possibilities exist: either we are
alone in the Universe or we are not.
Both are equally terrifying."
—Arthur C. Clarke

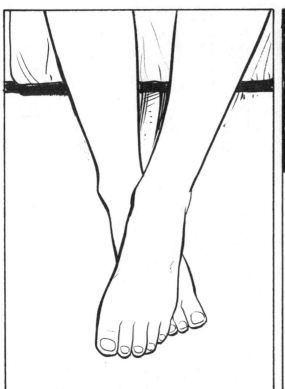

SIGH!

STANFORD. NAVY. RAN A MARATHON.

STOP PROFILING HER. SHE MUST BE GOOD OR LIBBY WOULDN'T HAVE SET ME UP WITH HER.

I'M NOT PROFILING, I'M CHECKING HER CREDENTIALS.

SHE LOOKS SWEATY.

SIT DOWN.

YOU KNOW WHO SWEATS A LOT? FELONS. LIARS.

CONTAGIOUS PSYCHOS.

NOT HELPING.

SAMANTHA?

YES.

HI. I'M DR. KIM.

HI.

SO YOU'RE A FRIEND OF LIBBY'S. SHE SPOKE VERY HIGHLY OF YOU.

I WORK AT HER JUNKYARD.

LIBBY SCRAP.

=HEH= YEAH, YOU COULD CALL IT THAT.

SO TELL ME ABOUT YOUR HEADACHES.

THEY COME AND GO.

GRRPH!

HOW BAD ARE THEY, ON A SCALE OF ONE TO TEN?

UMM, SEVEN ...MAYBE.

LOOK TO YOUR RIGHT.

OH STOP YOUR HUFFIN' AND PUFFIN', SHE'S NOT GOING TO HURT ME.

=sigh=

PUT YOUR HANDS UP... PUSH OUT AGAINST MY HANDS. ANY NAUSEA OR SENSITIVITY TO LIGHT?

LIKE A MIGRAINE? NO.

ANY PROBLEMS WITH BALANCE?

NO.

SO I'M GOING TO LOOSEN YOUR GOWN NOW AND LISTEN...TO...

WHAT HAPPENED HERE?

IRAQI PRISON.

YOU WERE IN THE MILITARY?

MARINES.

I WAS NAVY, SIX YEARS. DID YOU SUFFER ANY HEAD INJURIES?

I GUESS, THEY HIT ME EVERY DAY FOR TEN MONTHS.

IS THAT WHERE YOU GOT THESE SCARS ON THE BACK OF YOUR SCALP?

I SUPPOSE. THEY LIKED TO WORK THE BACKSIDE SO THE FRONT LOOKED OKAY ON CAMERA. Y'KNOW... FOR NATO.

DID YOU RECEIVE MEDICAL ATTENTION AFTER CAPTIVITY?

NINE WEEKS IN THE HOSPITAL, A YEAR OF REHAB.

THAT'S A LOT TO GO THROUGH ALONE.

I WASN'T ALONE.

I WAS NEVER ALONE.

50

ANYTHING ELSE GOING ON, OTHER THAN THE HEADACHES? ANY UNUSUAL SYMPTOMS OR ABNORMALITIES YOU MIGHT HAVE NOTICED?

CLICK!

NOPE. EVERYTHING IS NORMAL.

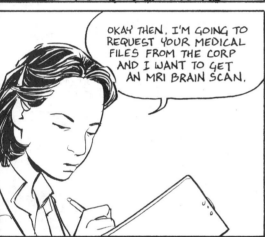

OKAY THEN, I'M GOING TO REQUEST YOUR MEDICAL FILES FROM THE CORP AND I WANT TO GET AN MRI BRAIN SCAN.

CAN'T YOU JUST GIVE ME SOMETHING FOR THE HEADACHES? I DON'T WANT ANY MORE DRAMA IN MY BRAIN.

I CAN GIVE YOU SOMETHING TO MASK THE PAIN BUT WE SHOULD FIND OUT WHAT'S CAUSING IT. THE SCAN WOULD BE VERY HELPFUL.

I'LL THINK ABOUT IT.

TWEET

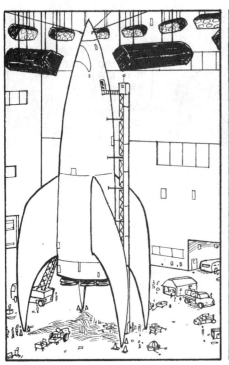

THE X9 IS THE ROCKET OF THE FUTURE, MR. HERGE! IT CAN TAKE OFF AND LAND SAFELY ON ANY SURFACE ANGLE UNDER 30 DEGREES, THE ATOMIC FUEL WILL LAST 10,000 YEARS AND THE PAYLOAD IS TWICE THAT OF THE X8.

DOES IT HAVE WI-FI?

OF COURSE.

EXCELLENT.

THE BOARD IS QUITE PLEASED WITH THE PROGRESS OF OUR COMMERCIAL PROGRAMS, MR. WALDEN. WHAT WE WANT TO KNOW IS—

WHERE ARE WE WITH THE NEUTRON PROJECT?

READY TO TEST. WOULD YOU LIKE TO SEE IT?

YES.

WE'VE LOCATED THE CENTER OF THE MOST ACTIVE REGION. I'M PURCHASING THE LAND FROM A PRIVATE OWNER AND WE'LL MOVE QUICKLY TO INSTALL THE NP-2.

IT'S... SMALLER THAN I THOUGHT IT'D BE.

STEALTH AND MOBILITY ARE KEY FACTORS—

FOR A DEFENSE WEAPON DESIGNED TO BRING DOWN ANY AND ALL FLYING OBJECTS.

INCLUDING UFOS?

ESPECIALLY UFOS!

COUGH! COUGH!
COUGH! COUGH!
COUGH! COUGH!

ACK!
ACK!

WASSUP?

MAN, IT'S HOT OUT HERE.

I HATE TO ADMIT IT, LARRY, BUT I THINK YOU'RE RIGHT.

ABOUT WHAT?

LEVERAGING THE OLD WOMAN WITH THE GIRL. I THINK IT'S THE FASTEST WAY FORWARD.

SERIOUSLY?

YEAH.

NOW YOU'RE TALKING!

WE DON'T HAVE A CHOICE. WE HAVE THREE DAYS TO CLOSE THIS DEAL OR WE'RE OUT OF A JOB.

SHE'LL GET US FIRED!

IT'S HER OR US.

WE HAVE NO CHOICE!!

CHARLIE PARKER WAS A GENIUS!

NO, HE WASN'T. HE HE WAS A SCALE RUNNER WITH NO REGARD FOR MELODY. HE AND GILLESPIE STARTED BEBOP AND BROUGHT ABOUT THE END OF THE BIG BAND ERA. THEY SHOULD HAVE BEEN ARRESTED ... BOTH OF THEM!

TELL ME YOU DID NOT JUST COMPARE A RUNAWAY HORN TO THE RAVEL OF GUITAR!

CHARLIE PARKER WAS NOT A SCALE RUNNER! HE JUST HEARD MORE MELODIES THAN US. LIKE HENDRIX. GENIUSES, BOTH OF 'EM!

BZZ

PARKER NEVER PLAYED ANYTHING FITZGERALD COULDN'T SING. THAT'S CALLED MELODY, SEE? AND... AND...

WITHOUT PARKER WE WOULDN'T HAVE HAD MILES DAVIS!

MILES DAVIS

I KNOW WHAT YOU'RE DOIN'! EVERY TIME YOU WANT TO DISTRACT ME, YOU BAIT ME WITH CHARLIE PARKER! WHAT ARE YOU TRYING TO HIDE, HUH? TELL ME...

PUTT! PUTT! PUTT!

CATO

THAT GIRL NEEDS TO GET OUT OF THE SUN.

WHO YOU TALKIN' TO?

OH! HEY LIBBY. I DIDN'T HEAR YOU RIDE UP.

YOU SHOULD THINK ABOUT WEARING A HAT OUT HERE.

I'M FINE. WHAT BRINGS YOU OUT TO THE YARD?

FELLA JUST CALLED WITH A DONOR CAR. YOU GOT TIME TO PICK IT UP?

SURE.

YOU NEED A WIDE-BRIM HAT IN THIS SUN, SAM. I'M JUST SAYIN'.

LIBBY, SERIOUSLY. I'VE LIVED MY WHOLE LIFE IN THE DESERT.

IT'S 116 TODAY ...IN THE SHADE!

JIMINY CRACKERS!

I'M USED TO IT.

SUIT YOURSELF. I'M GOING BACK TO THE HOUSE AND POP A TOP.

SAVE ME ONE FOR WHEN I GET BACK.

I'LL HAVE A ROOT BEER.

I'M NOT USED TO THE DESERT. I NEED JUNGLE.

JUNGLES ARE FULL OF BUGS AND NAKED MEN.

YOU MEAN PROTEIN.

GROSS.

CIRCLE OF LIFE.

STILL GROSS.

CRUNCH, CRUNCH.

PUKE PUKE.

RHINOPLASTY

RUMBLE! RUMBLE!

FOR LEASE
Callahan Realty

HEY LIBBY. ARE YOU SURE ABOUT THIS DONOR CAR? IT LOOKS NEW, SO I RAN THE PLATE AND IT'S A RENTAL FROM McCARRAN. SO... I'M THINKING THAT WAS A PRANK CALL.

WELL, SHOOT, I GUESS WE'VE BEEN PUNKED. SORRY, SAM. HEY, GOTTA GO, I'M AT THE SALON GETTING WAXED,

RIPPP!

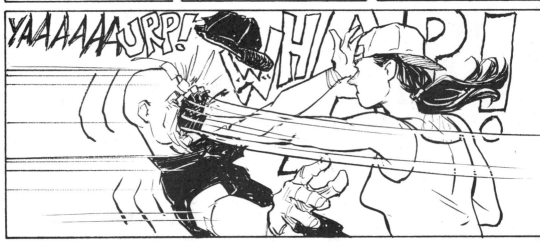

GO!GO!GO!

SCREECH!!!

WHAT WAS THAT ALL ABOUT?

HE JUST TRIED TO *KIDNAP* YOU!

I KNOW, BUT ... WHY?!

I DON'T CARE WHY. I WANT TO BITE HIS FACE OFF.

YOU NEED TO START CARRYING YOUR GUN.

I DON'T NEED A GUN, I'M A MARINE.

THOSE MEN ARE DANGEROUS.

WAR IS DANGEROUS. THOSE GUYS ARE JUST...

CONFUSING.

REALLY CONFUSING.

61

SLAM!

I KNEW THOSE GUYS WERE TROUBLE THE MINUTE I SAW THEM... STREET THUGS WHO GREW UP TO BECOME SOMEBODY'S GOONS.

THAT SAYS A LOT ABOUT THE MAN WHO HIRED THEM.

UGH... THIS HEAT.

WHAT'S THE MATTER?

MY HEAD.

UH OH.

DO YOU WANT A COLD TOWEL? WATER?

MAYBE YOU SHOULD GET INTO BED BEFORE IT GETS TOO BAD, THINK YOU CAN MAKE IT?

SAM? WHAT CAN I DO TO HELP YOU?

Please stop talking.

WHY DOESN'T SHE TURN ON THE LIGHTS?

I DON'T KNOW. MAYBE SHE'S ASLEEP.

THEN WHAT ARE WE WAITING FOR?

JUST MAKING SURE SHE'S ALONE. WE'RE NOT GOING TO UNDERESTIMATE HER AGAIN.

**"The story of life is quicker than
the blink of an eye. The story
of love is hello, goodbye."
—Jimi Hendrix**

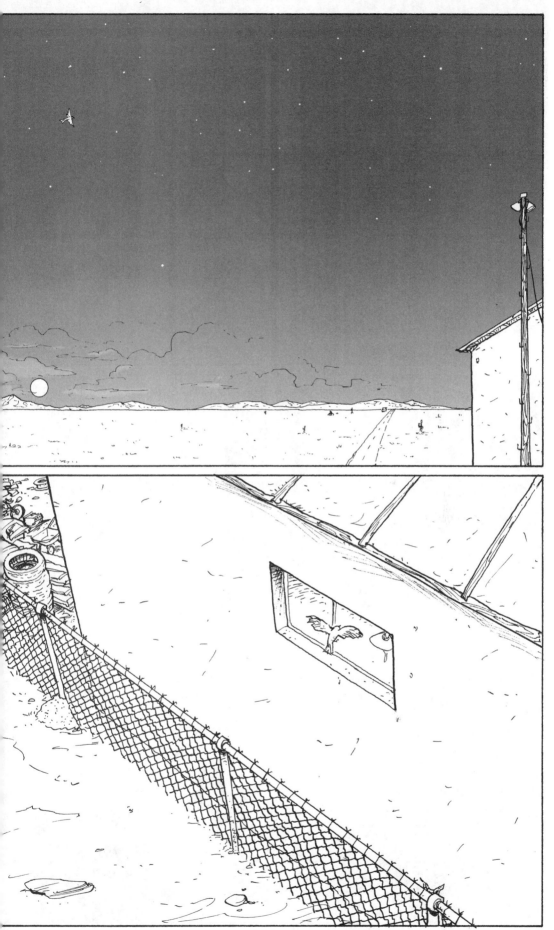

> CHEEP!
> CHEEP!

WHAT ARE **YOU** LOOKIN' AT?

> CHEEP!

SAME TO YOU, LADY.

71

WHAT'S YOUR NAME? SEEMS ONLY FAIR I SHOULD KNOW THE NAME OF THE GUY WHO TRIED TO KIDNAP ME.

WHAT'S YOUR NAME?!

VICTOR.

OKAY THEN... VICTOR... ARE YOU ARMED?

No.

THE LAST GUY I SAW SITTING IN THE SUN LIKE THIS BLEW HIMSELF UP AND TOOK TWO OF MY BUDDIES WITH HIM.

ARE YOU WEARING A BOMB, VICTOR?

WHY ON EARTH WOULD I WEAR A FRIKKIN' BOMB?

DO YOU HAVE A BOMB?!

NO!

WHY SHOULD I BELIEVE YOU? YOU TRIED TO KIDNAP ME YESTERDAY AND TODAY YOUR CAR IS PARKED BESIDE THE ROAD I HAVE TO DRIVE ON! IS THERE A BOMB IN YOUR CAR, VICTOR?! LARRY SCREWED UP THE DETONATOR, DIDN'T HE?!

NO, GEEZ! LISTEN...

SIT! DOWN!

HANDS UP! NOW!

WHOA.

I'M NOT ARMED, OKAY? I DON'T HAVE A BOMB! I DON'T EVEN KNOW WHERE TO BUY ONE, AND IF I DID I WOULDN'T GET IT AND IF I *DID* GET IT I SURE WOULDN'T BRING IT OUT HERE IN THE MIDDLE OF NOWHERE AND SIT ON IT!

YOU TRIED TO TAKE ME HOSTAGE!

WELL, YEAH. BUT WE WEREN'T GOING TO HURT YOU. WE JUST NEEDED A LITTLE LEVERAGE TO GET THE CONTRACT SIGNED.

AND... IT WAS A BAD IDEA. I SEE THAT NOW.

WHO *ARE* YOU GUYS?! WHO DO YOU *WORK* FOR?

HE CALLS HIMSELF WALDEN. THAT'S ALL I KNOW.

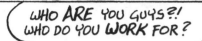

YOU'RE NOT WITH HIS COMPANY?

NO. LARRY AND I ARE WORK-FOR-HIRE. TO TELL YOU THE TRUTH, HE'S OUR FIRST JOB. BUT IF WE DON'T GET THAT CONTRACT SIGNED BY MONDAY, WE'RE FIRED!

SO YOU'RE JUST A COUPLE OF IDIOTS.

UHH...

WHAT ARE YOU DOING OUT HERE? WHERE'S YOUR BUDDY LARRY?

I'M WAITING FOR HIM.

HE'S NOT AT MY HOUSE, IS HE? OR LIBBY'S?

NO. YOU WOULDN'T BELIEVE ME IF I TOLD YOU.

TRY ME.

LARRY WAS... ABDUCTED LAST NIGHT ... BY A FLYING SAUCER.

ARE YOU KIDDING ME?! CRAP!!

I KNEW YOU WOULDN'T BELIEVE ME.

NO NO... I BELIEVE YOU!

DID YOU SEE THE ALIENS? THE LITTLE GREEN MEN NAMED BIK AND BEEP?

YOU'RE MAKING FUN OF ME.

NO I'M NOT!

THIS ISN'T FUNNY, LADY! MY PARTNER IS **GONE**! OKAY? JUST... GONE!

WAIT...

WHEN YOU SAY LARRY IS YOUR PARTNER... DO YOU MEAN BUSINESS, OR...?

I'M ENGAGED TO HIS SISTER. IF I LOSE HIM, SHE'LL NEVER FORGIVE ME.

THAT MIGHT BE A GOOD THING.

SORRY.

BAD JOKE.

LARRY'S NOT SO BAD ONCE YOU GET TO KNOW HIM. HE TAKES IN DOGS OFF THE STREET, FINDS HOMES FOR THEM.

THEN YOU HAD TO GO PUNCH HIM IN THE FACE!

HE WAS TRYING TO *KIDNAP* ME!

YOU DIDN'T HAVE TO BREAK HIS **NOSE**!

I'M SORRY!

HE SNORES BAD ENOUGH AS IT IS!

AAAGH

THIS GUY'S AN IDIOT.

NO, THE OTHER ONE'S AN IDIOT.

THIS ONE...

NEEDS ANGER MANAGEMENT.

GOOD JUMPER THOUGH.

MIKEY... DON'T YOU WONDER...

WHY ARE THEY GOING TO ALL THIS TROUBLE TO GET THEIR HANDS ON THE JUNKYARD?

CHINATOWN?

YOU MEAN MINERAL RIGHTS AND WATERWAYS? NOT LIKELY.

I THINK THEY'RE LOOKING...

UP.

AIR SPACE IS CONTROLLED BY THE GOVERNMENT.

TELL THAT TO THE UFOS.

WE DO SEEM TO HAVE A LOT OF FIREFLIES IN OUR SKIES.

YEAH, WE DO, DON'T WE?

SO, WHO CAME FIRST...

THE VISITORS OR THE MAN WHO WANTS THE GROUND BELOW THEM?

I READ ON THE INTERNET THAT ALIENS BROUGHT FIRST LIFE TO EARTH.

I SAW A MOVIE THAT SAID ALIENS WERE GOING TO RISE UP FROM THE GROUND AND KILL US.

SAM... ALIENS AREN'T THE PROBLEM.

I KNOW, MIKEY.

I KNOW.

STAY!

OOF!

DUDE...

WHATEVER'S HAPPENING HERE, YOU'RE ON THE WRONG SIDE OF IT.

YOU NEED TO GO BACK WHERE YOU CAME FROM.

I'M NOT LEAVING WITHOUT LARRY.

WELL... THEN DON'T WAIT FOR HIM OUT HERE, YOU'LL DIE OF SUNSTROKE BEFORE NOON.

WHERE DID YOU LEARN TO HIT LIKE THAT?

YOU DON'T WANT TO KNOW.

≋SPIT!≋

I REALLY DID SEE A UFO LAST NIGHT.

A FLYING SAUCER.

I BELIEVE YOU.

YOU'VE SEEN ONE, TOO, HAVEN'T YOU?

THEY'RE OUT HERE!

THAT'S WHY WALDEN WANTS THE PROPERTY!

YOU DON'T KNOW THIS GUY. HE DOESN'T TAKE NO FOR AN ANSWER. YOU CAN'T TAKE HIM ON ALONE.

HE DOESN'T KNOW ME.

I'M NOT ALONE.

"In an age of hope men looked up
at the night sky and saw "the heavens".
In an age of hopelessness they
call it simply "space".
—Peter Kreeft

88

LEWIS WALDEN.

IS LIBBY AROUND?

MR. WALDEN

NO. SHE HAS AN OFFICE DOWNTOWN.

AT THE HARDWARE STORE?

RIGHT.

I MADE YOUR BOSS A GENEROUS OFFER ON THIS PROPERTY AND SHE TURNED ME DOWN.

SO I HEARD.

I WAS WONDERING WHY.

WHY TURN DOWN GOOD MONEY TO HANG ONTO THIS BARREN PLOT OF LAND? WHY WOULD SHE DO THAT?

SO I DID A LITTLE RESEARCH AND YOU KNOW WHAT I FOUND?

YOUR MEDICAL FILE.

SERGEANT, YOU'RE A MESS.

90

POST TRAUMATIC STRESS, EXTENSIVE SCAR TISSUE UP THE BACK AND NECK, LOSS OF HEARING IN ONE EAR, BONE GRAFTS FOR A FRACTURED SKULL...

AND...THE ONE THAT'S GOING TO GET YOU...

INTRACRANIAL NEOPLASM.

HOW DO YOU KNOW? MY RECORDS ARE SEALED.

NOT FROM ME.

IT'S YOUR FAULT, ISN'T IT?

WHAT?

YOU'RE THE REASON LIBBY WON'T SELL THIS PLACE. SHE'S KEEPING IT FOR YOU.

THIS ISN'T A JUNKYARD—

IT'S A HOSPICE!

I CAN HELP YOU.

FLY YOU OUT TO JOHNS HOPKINS TONIGHT—

FULL MEDICAL PROFILE AND EVALUATION BY THE BEST DOCTORS IN THE WORLD—

WHATEVER IT TAKES, I WILL PAY FOR IT.

ALL YOU HAVE TO DO IS TELL LIBBY TO SELL THIS LAND TO ME.

TELL HER...

AND I WILL SAVE YOU.

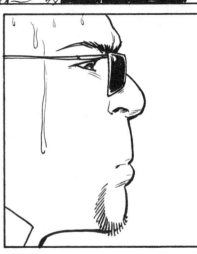

OR NOT.

WE'LL SET UP OUTSIDE THE FENCE FOR NOW. YOU HAVE 24 HOURS TO DECIDE.

SET UP WHAT?

GOOD DAY, SARGEANT.

93

94

BIK!

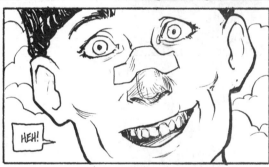

HEH!

I KNEW IT E.T.'S NOTHING BUT A HARMLESS PUP!

BIK!

HEY THERE, LITTLE BUDDY. WELCOME TO EARTH.

BIK! BIK!

WELL OKAY THEN. I KNOW HOW THIS WORKS, I SAW THE BOWIE MOVIE— COME FOR THE WATER, STAY FOR THE GIRLS, RIGHT? I DON'T BLAME YOU. IT'S ALL PERFECTLY NATURAL. YEP... I CAN HANDLE THIS.

SO...

WHERE ARE WE?